CW00407300

The Foresters' Story

We walked deeper and deeper into the forest
With,
Darkness like a cloak,
Surrounding.
Icy fingers
Play down our spines,
Breath comes shallow
From the icy bite
While we search for your home
On this, the coldest night.

Beginnings

I read once that every journey starts with a single step, but this journey seems to have no beginning and no end, and instead we need to step into it at a random place because my story is random, and yet at the same time it is entwined with the eternal story of the very first forests. It exists at once in the moment and in all time.

The day started cold and continued like every other Sunday. The whole family woke early and poured downstairs into the only room that was warm: the little lounge that was our sanctuary on cold winter days. Father was there, which was rare because usually he would have gone to work long before we were up and about. For us, Sunday was a joyous day, apart from the big, boring interlude that came after breakfast, when it was off to church. I would fill these two hours with daydreaming, daydreaming of a time of warriors and battles and heroes. This was the place in my head I escaped to as the man in white droned on.

Then after the church came Sunday lunch, the best meal of the week. Meat, veg, gravy, and always a hot pudding on a cold winter's day. The fire was lit, the kitchen was warm and the small living room was converted into a dining room with a big table around which we would all sit and talk and laugh. Then in the afternoon we would go for a walk. On this particular day we were going to Grandfather's house. Wrapped up in warm coats, mitten strings held fast and hands cosy inside, warm woolly hats on our heads, and we were ready to go. The ground outside was crisp with frost, and we walked down to where the bridge spanned the little road at the entrance to the village through which trains had once rumbled along the cutting that was carved into the chalk, with banks that seemed to me to be as high as cliffs. I could imagine the steam trains puffing along and me being the engine driver, blowing the horn as I raced through the cutting.

Looking back, it seems such a long walk for small legs, but the excitement of going to Grandfather's house was worth it. We walked past the old station which now lay derelict, and then to the gate. Beyond the gate a small meadow opened up, marked by a grass track that had been walked by many feet for many years. In spring and summer this was the meadow where we often played. There was the buttercup game – holding the golden flower under your chin to see if you liked butter, making daisy chains and seeing who could make the longest, and then of course a game we called Old Granny Flipper Flopper. We would hold the plantain stem, bend its head and shout:

Old Granny Flipper Flopper jumped out of bed,
She looked out the window
And off popped her head.

And we would pull the loop forward and the plantain head would fire off the stem!

Past the meadow we could catch glimpses of smoke through the trees, for this was where Grandfather lived, in a small single storey wooden cabin. A gentle light could be seen from a kerosene lamp burning in the window and when you entered the house, you were assailed by the smell of wood smoke, a smell that even today fills me with thoughts of home and safety.

Today Grandfather was sitting next to the fire, whittling a stick with his trusty penknife, the one he always carried with him, the discarded bits being thrown into the fire. From where I stood, I could see he was making a small figure out of a piece of hawthorn, a tree I recognised for I used to spend many days out in the woods and there I would learn the stories of all the trees, their names, their legends and the strange creatures that lived amongst them. Some of these creatures you might recognise from everyday life but there were also creatures that came out of Grandfather's imagination, or so I believed then. I can still remember that strange little man made out of a hawthorn bough, with tufts of grass for his hair.

When Grandfather looked up, his smile brightened his face. It was full of warmth and love, but there was also a glint of mischief in his eye.

Nine years later

If there was just one moment, one memory that fills your deepest dream, that sends shivers down your spine which one would it be? Which one takes you back to that moment that changes everything? Each of us has that one singular moment without which life would be so very different. Would you be sitting reading this, and would I have even written these pages without that one particular, life-changing moment? And yet that moment may have meant nothing to all the other actors in your play. Maybe they do not have even the slightest recollection of it, but still it contains every important thing, all that you love and all that you fear.

We walked slowly along the track on this moon-bright night with the trees folding over us as it became denser. We had left the place where we had built the bonfire earlier on and now headed for the heart of the forest, the glade where all the trees seemed to congregate around the edges. As the forest started to get lighter again, Grandfather stopped short. I did not notice and carried on for a few more steps. "Wait," Grandfather hissed and I became still.
I looked up and there in front of us was a stag sitting right across the track. The moon hung bright above him.

"Can we go closer?" I whispered but Grandfather's brief glance was enough to tell me to stay quiet and still.

The stag did not move. It felt as if time was standing still, and the whole forest had gone quiet. The silence bit into me and held me. It scared me a little, perhaps; certainly it confused me. I had a deep longing to know why the stag was blocking us from going through the forest, for this was my grandfather's home. This was the way he always came, and he was never afraid, always confident, always strong. Tonight, though, Grandfather seemed unable to make a decision, and the stag never stopped looking into his eyes. Eventually Grandfather turned away and as I watched, just for a briefest of seconds, the stag settled deeper into the earth. Then it looked up to the Moon and a sigh echoed through the forest.

Many days passed. School was boring as usual and time dragged until I saw Grandfather again. It was a very different man who met me that day at the gates of the school. He had never visited me here before and I had never seen him this far from his beloved forest. "I need some help," he said. "And I have some things for you."
Back at his cabin, he gave me his books, and the journals in which he wrote his woodland lore and told me I would need them one day. I laughed at this: I was going to be a computer engineer and would never have need for the stories from the forest. Grandfather had smiled. "Even great engineers need time to grow," he said.
We sat long into the evening, under a clear sky, talking, listening to the wind in the trees and just enjoying the time together. These few hours seemed to last a lifetime and yet also to last no time at all: just moments out of time.

I never saw my grandfather again in this world, for that evening he had gone to bed and somewhen in the night had just died. My parents were sad and upset but seemed resigned to what had happened and it was many years later that I learned that he had been ill for a very long time. The funeral, in the little churchyard, in the village was full of people I did not know, and it all passed in such a blur and soon we were all back to everyday routines. The journals and books packed into a cupboard and almost but never quite forgotten.

School carried on for me and sometimes I would visit Grandfathers house in the woods, always alone and although I tried to keep it standing, as the years passed it slowly started to crumble away. I often cried as a teenager here, full of the angst that comes at that age but also for the loss of that calming voice. I would tell my grandfather of my life, always open and honest when alone. I would tell him of trying to fit in with all the groups and cliques and how I always felt alone and out of place.

School finished for me and yes I did become a computer engineer and with it came the house, marriage and all the trappings that go with this world. I climbed the mountain of success in this world and from the top all I could see was greed and longing for more and all I felt was loss. Loss of simplicity and loss of care. Seduced by want, until at my lowest ebb I broke.

So here I found myself in a small caravan home in a muddy field.

Dreaming the Fawn

Scritch scratch, scritch scratch on the paper as I try to hold onto the dream. In the dark of night, not daring to light the torch I hold in case it extinguishes the last fleeting memories. I hold out my arms, straight, into the darkness and try to pull back the tatters of my dream as it flees through the crack in reality. Holding tight to nothingness, I catch a glimpse of another world this world, but not the one I see outside the window.

I have been parked here, in my little caravan, for a month now in a very muddy field. The field is slowly being transformed: each trudging day, more and more trees are being planted. The field lies on the outskirts of Swindon, where the main road is noisy and the Honda factory drones day and night. It will become an oasis of calm in the never-ending noise that we call progress.

I had been here on and off for six months, planning and preparing, and now in the depths of winter, here alone, I started planting the twenty thousand trees that would become a new forest. Each day a new circle was planted. No straight lines, so that the forest would eventually look natural, with shrubs and wide tracks meandering through it. I could imagine that as the years passed, families would walk these woods, dogs at their heels, sniffing out the creatures that would make this their home. A forest in the middle of a spawling concrete jungle. I am good at planting trees: less good at trying to write down my dream.

Words seem inadequate. So instead of writing, I turn on the torch and find the journal given to me by Grandfather, and the other two books that bring me happiness: The Man who Planted Trees, and Walden, my go-to books during the long evenings in the caravan.

I write a small note into Grandfather's book about how the trees had tricked me again.

"Today I planted a small block of oak trees against the hawthorns I had planned for the western edge, close to the road fence. I had filled my planting bag with just the oak trees I required and made the long walk to the section I wanted to plant. I have been doing this work now for many years and soon got into the rhythm of digging and planting. The task is therapeutic, almost calming: push spade into ground, pull it out, plant and then heel in the tree. Again and again and again.

Every tree I pulled from the bag was an oak tree and soon I had all hundred in the ground. I went to collect the stakes and shelters for the tiny trees, but as I walk up the lines I could see that the trees had a mind of their own, because for every oak there was an ash, and for every ash there was a birch, and all along the scalloped edge of the plantation a triangle had formed. Oak, then Ash, and at the apex of the triangle a hawthorn and outlying each one a birch, just as Grandfather's book had shown in the strange notation he had always used.

'The Golden Triangle' he had called it in the book. A small note in the margin read: "Oak for the people, hawthorn for the fae, and binding them forever Yggdrasil, the ash".

As I hold onto the final remnants of the dream I have one simple image still in my head: an image of the forest I am creating here in this noisy place. In the dream it is quiet, the trees grown large. I am on one of the tracks where the moon shines down and there in the middle of the track is a fawn. The fawn is aglow as if lit from within, outshining even the light of the moon, just standing there, and as I stare so it stares back. It does not seem afraid and then I see that surrounding the fawn are numerous other creatures, ethereal, almost ghostly. As I watch, the fawn lies down upon the track and slowly seems to melt into the earth. It does not disappear but simply falls away into the ground, and as it falls the other creatures slowly become more solid. They are here now and real; and as they become real, so I can hear a beating, like a heartbeat. It resonates inside me, and my heart seems to catch onto the same rhythm and a peace and calmness falls over me. I have never experienced this feeling before but I imagine it is how a shaman feels when travelling the liminal realms, or a priest when in the presence of the divine. It is a feeling of pure eternity, of universal one-ness and truth.

Interlude 1

Many years later
Hannah's story.

A whirlwind has taken over my life. A whirlwind I never saw coming. It came with no warning sound and blasted pure change through my life. I can feel everything super-acutely, as if I have just awoken after twenty years from a coma. I am planting a little triangular woodland in the corner of a field, overlooking Silbury Hill, with Avebury away in the distance, and my heart is full of light. I'm finally here with my wild forester.

Two months ago, the window I was looking through was so tinted that it was perpetually an overcast miserable day outside, even in a heatwave. The air was constantly recycled: the windows did not open. This office is where I have spent twenty years, doing a job that feels irrelevant and pointless. The trouble is, you grow used to such routine until the longing for change becomes remote, a lost thing somewhere on the periphery of each day. I could stand here a thousand years and it would always stay the same
Safe, comfortable, soulless.

When I was a child I read stories from the woodlands, stories stirring feelings that at the time I did not understand. These were the stories of the wild places, of fairy, woodsman and animals. They brought forth drawings that I filled sketchbooks with and in those drawings resided the stories I made up and told myself. Magical stories full of creatures, both real and of my own imagination, yet years later I found they were also part of the myths and legends of this land that I lived. I found friends in the story, creatures of night, clothed with their halos, clothed with the light.

My storybook friends became the only constant after school shut for the day my bedroom a sanctuary and place to let the tales unfold. I was alive there in those tales, alive and free from the worry of fitting in, of school and of the world talked about every evening as my father watched the news. But like all good stories they one day had to end, and it was my time to find my way in the world. I like most people did find my way and as grandmother had always told me, when I was at my lowest, "Life's like that get over it" and so I did, well I tried.

"Well, I tried." I have just read that back and it makes me smile now because I did try at first. I went to work, I bought a house and suddenly I was a grown-up. I worked in a huge office block at a job I hated and that made no sense to me whatsoever. After a while I stopped trying. I would daydream of my own world and stare out of the window waiting for the day to end. And as time passed, I became expert in 8 full hours of daydreaming. Eventually I think, time turned, the world changed, and at last I found my rabbit hole to fall into and out of that artificial world forever.

That rabbit hole appeared but not like in any of my stories, no white horse to carry me off into the wild and free places, no raggle taggle gypsy and definitely no riches and house of my dreams. No, my knight in shining armour turned up in a muddy field, his sword a spade and his chariot an old and rusty Landrover.

I had been walking that day over the fields that surround Kennet long barrow, looking at all the earthworks surrounding the ancient landscape of Avebury, with its amazing stone circle and processional avenue and had tried to find a high point to look out over Silbury Hill. I had found a point at which I could see the hill but it was in a field where a lone forester was planting trees, huge sweeping curves and I watched a while wondering what this place would look like in the years to come and what sort of trees were being planted.

I must have stood for quite a time, back in a daydreaming world as when I looked up the forester is stood just in front of me, he smiles and says, "You were miles away" I smile and say "sorry". An auspicious start for a conversation, I think. But talk we do, and that talk lasted all the rest of the day, you may wonder what we said and for most I cannot remember until we spoke of dreams and stories of folk songs and of magic until eventually he asks a question that has been almost asked before, "Are you my artist" and he looks away embarrassed and a small part of my old life that was slipping away thinks "Not a bad chat up line" and then I smile for I hope so and I hope the stories can bind us together in a new tale. Later he talks of dreams and the dream of the fawn.

The dream of the tale of the Fawn

A forest is just a forest, devoid of experience, devoid of life without the creatures that inhabit it. At the beginning of the world when all the land was the first forest, each tree and shrub communicated with one other through root and leaf. There were hardly any people, and just a few of the fae; so in essence, the forest was empty and alone. It stood for thousands of years unchanging, each day, each year just the same. And over the years, the trees lost their ability to speak, for there was nothing for them to talk about.

The Sun God continued to beat down and Mother Moon cast her light at night but they had become disconnected to the Earth down below. At the centre of the forest stood the World Tree, Yggdrasil. Its sap, moved like blood between the heavens and the lower realms, passing always through the Earth at its centre. As time passed the great tree's sap started falling from the leaf and pooling at its feet, red with life, the tears of a forest grown old and tired.

For the first time in many a year the Sun God and Mother Moon looked down upon the Earth hearing and feeling the anguish of Yggdrasil and they saw that all was not well, that the Earth was an unhappy place, the joy and the wonder missing, for they had grown weary and neglectful.

The Sun God and Mother Moon called out to each other, but the voice that replied was the voice of their only child, their daughter Gaia. "For you to see and understand your creation, you must give something of yourself, something you love; for only through pure sacrifice will you learn the truth of your own being." And with these words she leapt towards the Earth and as she fell a tail of pure light streaked across the sky and a booming sounded through the heavens. All the Earth, trees, people and fae looked to the stars as this new light rained down on them and with it came Wind and Fire to join the Earth and Water.

The first forest took its first breath and beneath the World Tree, the child of the Moon and Sun stood, clothed in the red of the fire and the stars of the sky. And out of this first breath stepped the fawn. She was born to the Earth but her sacrifice for the Earth was still to come, for she was to be the heart and soul of all things. As she stood, she dreamed, and as she dreamed so all the creatures of the future forest appeared as haloes around her.

"You know what must be," the fawn said to the World Tree and the tree sadly drew the fawn down into its roots, and so the sacrifice was given. For each bone of her beautiful body was given to each of the creatures, her blood to their veins and eventually all that was left was her beating heart which Yggdrasil took down the long roots to the centre of the Earth and there it beats, audible still to all who want to hear it.

Can you ever be alone in the woods?

Planting trees can be a very meditative experience and when you have been doing it day in day out for months on end, you become lost in the woods to be. And as you plant, often a feeling comes upon you as you push spade into earth, that you are not alone, that someone is walking next to you. They watch you as you dig, mostly unseen but occasionally you catch a glimpse out of the corner of your eye. A figure, a creature: a hybrid of the two. The first time it happens, you jump back, afraid, waking from the daydream that you no longer recall and once again find yourself alone.

Days can pass before it happens again, and you start to wonder if being alone is healthy for you. You question your reality, and you start to laugh at your own flights of fancy, but deep in your heart, you know something was there with you. And then it happens again, and you feel the woods change. Are you seeing the woods that were, or those that will be? Unsettled and afraid, you turn, and there, standing right beside you, is a woman.

"You are not real; you are not real," I repeat as a mantra to the woman who walks beside me. She is tall, well over six feet, and broad:, not fat just large, with hair the colour of straw. She wears clothes of the brightest green and they shimmer with the sunlight that is filtering through the huge trees that have been growing for hundreds of years. My gait lengthens as I try to get out of the forest and yet I seem to have walked for ages, and the trees are getting denser and denser. I stop and turn to face my fear, and as I stop the world turns once again and the woman is gone and so has the vast forest, and I am left with a single thought in my head. "What is real?" I hear it in a voice deep in resonance, female and almost familiar.

As the days go by all seems normal again in the wood to be, but the voice remains in my head, singing a siren song of loss and bereavement. The words lie heavy upon me. "What is real?" And with that thought comes the essential question, "Who am I?" and the inevitable "Is there any purpose to my life?". In the dark night I awaken, confused and alone in my little caravan. I know sleep will not be coming to me again this night so now I sit under the cold, starbright sky listening to the solitude of the night. I doze and dream, waken and doze some more and sometime just before dawn, I hear her once more, a call that goes through my very bones and once again I walk into the forest as was.

The first forest, without start or end, surrounds me, and I feel small within it. I can see a glimmer of the early morning light through the branches. I can touch each of the trees and know they are real even though it is impossible for them to be here. As I touch the trees, I can feel the beating heart of the forest breathing life into all things. I continue onwards until I find a small meadow, so much smaller than in my memories of this place. Just across the clearing is a familiar sight. But it cannot be here now, for this is Grandfather's house. I feel tears on my cheek as I hurry to the front door.

Inside the small wooden cabin, everything is exactly the same as my memory of the place, even down to the smell of woodsmoke. Sitting on the table is an open book, the one that now lives with me. I catch a glimpse of words, but they are not the same words, nor written in the same handwriting that Grandfather used. I sit down to read and with a shock recognise my own handwriting. It cannot be true; and yet I know it is true. I know also that Grandfather's house in my world slowly crumbles away.

"The night closed in tight today, earlier than normal, and the trees spoke of their fear of the machines just beyond the shadows. They talk of a world so out of balance with itself that the deer's heart has almost grown still, and they try to send out roots to that place to bring the first forests back home, to revive the lonely fawn."

Days out of time

I have stayed in the cabin waiting to see if the other me would return, but apart from the usual noises from the woodland, nothing or no-one appeared. I read more from the mystical journal until, feeling very tired, I moved to the bed in the small room and I fell very quickly into a deep sleep full of dreams. I dreamed that the cabin in which I slept slowly crumbled to become part of the forest until there was a place with no cabin, just a desolate wasteland without trees and animals. Then I dreamed of a forest full of life and children's laughter. When I awoke I felt even more tired than I had the night before. The sunlight glinted through the window and knowing sleep would not come to me again, I get up.

Back in the main room of the cabin, sunlight streams through the window. Putting the kettle on the stove, I brew a pot, and turn once again to the journal.

"The People and the Fae turned up together today, something unheard of before and I immediately knew something terrible must have happened. We sat outside on the step, the two people, dark-skinned and dressed in fur, and the two Fae elders - a jumble of twigs and moss with glowing coal-black eyes. We spoke in the language of the trees and as we talked I could tell that the whole forest had become silent and still. We all knew that every creature, plant and tree was listening, waiting to pass the news on.

"The sounds are coming daily now," they tell me, "and the trees talk of roots becoming burnt and dying." I knew this but continued to listen as they poured forth the worries that all of us have had. "We cannot let them get closer to the first forest," I say at last, "because all creatures and plants have their first home here and each and every living thing sprang from this place." We know this truth here, in our small corner of the world. The trees and plants speak to us of the seed forest, a place where all creatures, trees and plants originated. This forest, my home, is the seed of the idea of all living things and now it is under threat.

I try to digest these words but find it all very difficult to understand as back in my world we create plants and trees, hybrids of all and even hybrid animals for our own pleasure. I have spent my life planting trees, grown from seed, not magically placed from other worlds, but I am starting to understand that this place is not my home, and these words are not my own, even though they are written by me.

A tale from Grandfathers journal

In the beginning, long before the Fawn, the Ash tree woke up and looked around. The first forest was silent and still and she felt alone. She sent out roots deep into the ground and branches up to the sky but finding no others like her, she sent branches out even further, beyond the forests and beyond the world itself and on those branches, she brought forth other realms held up by the branches. And each of these realms contained the idea of the first forest and within them the forests grew.

As the years passed, the Ash tree continued to grow, larger and deeper into the new realms and here on one of those realms she found a creature, an eagle also alone and dying. The Ash tree took the eagle and brought it to the first forest that held the secrets of its own creation, and it lay in her branches. Time passed slowly once more and as time passed so the eagle changed. The eagle took on the shape of a man and hanging there he called out,

"I know that I hang on a windy tree

Nine long nights here I be,

Wounded myself so I can see

The name of this ash

The sacred tree.

Thawa my name given to me,

Yggdrasil the ash and holy tree.

Walking the Other Worlds

At the centre of the forest, I now find myself in the meadow. It seems different. In the middle sits a tree so tall that I cannot see the top of it. I walk around it, knowing it to be an ash tree. It's bark is gnarled and the humps of its roots are the size of horses!. The trunk must be eight metres in girth and it grows high into the air before the first branch is visible. On the southern side I come across a hole in its trunk, a hole so big I could walk inside if I wanted to. When I stare inside it is like looking up into the night sky. I can see vast distances across the universe and the twinkling of a myriad of stars, yet these stars are not the same constellations as the ones I am used to seeing, for they are uniform, all of equal size and I cannot count their number.

The pull to walk inside this tree comes upon me, yet I hesitate as it would be like walking into an infinite, a void. And yet the pull is still there, stronger the closer I go. Deep in my heart I know that if I were to enter I would be torn into millions of pieces, scattered to the stars.

"You can go in if you like," a voice behind me says. "Nothing will happen, for it has already happened."

I turn quickly, for I had not heard anyone creeping up behind me, and there stood, even taller than I remembered, the woman from my dreams.

Startled, I ask her, "Why have you brought me here?"

"I did not bring you here: you have always been here." Her voice is low and deep, resonating inside me, seeming to come from all around. For the first time I notice that the pockets of her green dress are teeming with small animals and that there are birds' nest in her hair.

"That is a different me. It is not the me I know in my head."

"Was it not you that cut down the forest, that killed the animals and crushed the flowers underfoot?" she asks sweetly. There is no accusation in her words, just curiosity.

"No," I reply. "That was not me. I am the man who planted trees."

"And is it not you who planted the forests, who talked to the elders and who cared for the creatures?" she asks.

I stood before her silent then, for an idea was forming in my head. I looked back once again at the worlds swirling beyond the entrance to the great tree. Perhaps I am starting to understand a little. I ask my question without turning back to her. "I can only do what I can do in the place I am in; I have no sway over the others."

"Then why do you dream of them? Why is there sadness in your heart, and hatred and loathing, things that have no place in there, when your world is full of beauty?"

Interlude 2

Hannah

The stories align

We sit, my forester and I and talk of worlds and dreams and light, of love and laughter and try to remember the first story we ever heard. I tell him of The Magic Faraway Tree, and he tells me of the magic within the Ash tree and slowly the story comes together as all stories do, a piece from here, a plucked sentence from there and then it takes on a life of its own

At the centre of the wood, at the centre of the Earth, at the centre of the cosmos, lies a tree like no other. And at the heart of the tree lies a secret.

For here in this forest lay the first story, a story so old that through generations of telling has become the story from all lands, changed but still holding the memory of its first telling. Never written down, just passed through a thousand, million different worlds in a thousand different tongues, it is the story of love and loss, of passion and beauty. It is your story, and mine.

Thawa was reborn from the corpse of an eagle, a creature that had existed even before it knew it existed. Once upon a time, this being had lived far, far above the Earth, but it had longed to see the Earth and had changed into the shape of the eagle. The journey to the Earth had been so long and arduous that the poor eagle had eventually fallen from the skies almost dead but had been saved by Yggdrasil, the World Tree. Yggdrasil, upon seeing Thawa, wanted to know what it would be like to live in the world of the ground and through that longing there appeared, a form from the roots of her tree. This form was the shape of the man but larger and more rounded, and upon her head was hair the colour of the glowing sun and around her crowded the creatures that would one day be. For she had dreamed through eons of time the world as it was to be, but in all those dreams it was just her, with the tree watching on.

Knowing

I turn to look back at Gaia and in that moment she is old, haggard and frail. Her straw-yellow hair lies limp against her bony face and her once-shimmering eyes are clouded and grey. The creatures that all lived in her clothes, in her hair and in her hands, now lie at her feet. She reaches out a skeletal hand towards me and I step back – for now I am scared for her, and scared of her.

I turn away and face the tree once again, but that step has taken me perilously close to the edge of a precipice leading into the swirling mass of worlds.

"Why do you dream of them, why is your heart full of sadness, hatred and loathing, things that have no place in there, when your world is full of beauty?" she says again, and this time these words stop me, and I stand, looking in upon the universe, as still as the tree in front of me.

The stars become blurred as tears fill my eyes, and I feel so tired it is as if the weight of all those universes is on my shoulders alone. And as my tears flow, so the worlds in front of me start to move and to change. For the first time I feel the touch of Gaia, just a small hand on my shoulder, and I do not pull away for in that moment I can see.

I see the worlds forming from thoughts and from deeds, worlds formed in love and laughter, all of them arrayed in the web that pulsates out from this point and I am the slowly revolving cog at the centre of the wheel.

I see hope and sadness, longing and hate. A glint of light as another world starts, and in that one, I find need and want, but it sputters out as I watch, lost to the wheel once more. To my left I see another world afire with blues and golds, a collision of two worlds, and in it I see love,: two souls coming together and a third forming out of that love.

The wheel moves slowly as lights combine towards the central boiling cauldron of light that now seems to be beneath my feet and I know that lives are starting here, moving outwards as their own time passes, and then I see shooting stars as a life ends and moves back to the centre, a continuous flowing beauty of life.

A deep resonance fills my head and I hear a voice. I know it comes from Gaia, but it also surrounds me and all the worlds.

"I am Yggdrasil and I stand at the centre of the forest, the home place whence all others grow. I call all who will hear to return here at least once in their lives. Some may come in dreams, and some may walk in the first forest as you have done, but I summon all to come home and to bear witness. My gift to you is time: a time to change, for when you are here you are also the cog that connects to all of you. The whole you and not the fragmented one that Chaos created."

I understand now why I am here, and for the first time Grandfather's way of life, his gentle approach. For the mark he left behind was not the mark of brick and stone but the mark of family and love. I had spent many a day trying to hold his little wooden cabin together. I had longed to live there as an adult, but it had crumbled back into the forest and was gone forever.

"Nothing is ever gone forever: we remember everything." It is as if Gaia is in my head and I feel her hand upon my shoulder. Questions asked are answered immediately in my head and a myriad of thoughts and dreams and possibilities, so many but not too many for me to bear. They are stored away until the time is right. I turn back to Gaia and her hand falls from my shoulder. I look up into her face and I see just beauty, purity and love. Gone is the old crone and standing there looking at me is a young girl full of life and fun. Her hair shines like gold and her eyes sparkle with glee and in her own voice, quieter and more direct, she says, "When they ask, please tell them I am young and beautiful."

She holds out her hand then and in it is a small blue eggshell cracked in two, clean on the inside with small flecks of silver and gold, and when I stare closely the specks shimmer and glow with all the lights of the universe.

I take it from her and go to thank her but as I do so, I feel myself fall backwards into the void and as I fall, I hear her voice once more.

"Remember me…"

Going home

I have heard it said that a conceited person thinks the world revolves around them. I wonder what you would say of a person who believes that not just the world, but also the universe, revolves around them and then says that they have been to the centre and have been the cog around which all worlds collide. But this is the beginning for me now. I feel reborn as once again I find myself back home in a muddy field. I do not seem to have been missing for all the time I believed I was missing. You might wonder if all this was a dream. I would agree but for two things: I have a broken eggshell, gifted by Gaia in my hand, and I was not dropped back at this forest to be, but at the centre of the forest I had known as a child. I had walked past the place where Grandfather's house had stood and smiled as I saw it slowly crumbling away. I did not stay but hurried on to the village, which I half expected not to be there.

I had gone to my sister's home and begged a lift to the station and then perhaps some money to buy a ticket, when I realised, I had none. She of course took me home, back to here and as we arrived I could see the hurt and worry on her face about how I lived now. I told her not to worry, for Gaia, Mother Earth, was taking care of me and she smiled in that way you would smile at a small child who has found out Father Christmas is not real, a smile of pity. Then she asked if I had food to eat and whether I have a dry home, clean clothes and all the things a person needs to live comfortably. I answered that I did, that mine was a small life, quietly lived and it suited me. When she left, I made a pot of tea, and placed it on the wood burner to keep it warm. I had told myself that I would make a pot each day, just in case visitors came. I poured myself a cup and took out the journal Grandfather gave me all those years ago. Inside, I found that my own words about the first forest had appeared. I sat down to write my own account of the last few days.

Hours passed and the light dimmed as I wrote in the journal about my plans for the new wood and how at its centre there would be an open area, grassy and quiet, with the trees of the first forest: my gift to that forest and its guardians. I felt contented and suddenly wondered if my time to be a shooting star had come, as this was how my grandfather had been on that final day. I realised quite quickly that could not be the case, as I was still to meet the artist of whom I had so often dreamt. The one who created stories in paint and pencil, the one who interpreted the longings in my soul.

On this one night in this one universe, I slept without dreams and as the sun rose that morning I got up, ready for the day ahead. It was the first day, the only day that mattered, and I had trees to plant.

"But," I hear you say, "you saw Gaia. You went to the centre, where all knowledge is. Tell us everything has changed!" And yes, I will tell you everything has changed, that this world is a different place today and will continue to change. I will tell you the secrets of the universe if you want, I will tell you how to make everything better and give you the answers to your questions, but first I have a forest to plant.

So, spade in hand, I planted an Oak, not an idea of an Oak but an actual Oak, that will grow strong and true. It will stand tall and shelter all that need its shelter. Next to it I planted an Apple, not the idea of an Apple but an actual tree that will grow and feed nectar to the bees and fruit for the animals and people of the world. Next to that I planted an Ash, and I named it Yggdrasil, for this tree will grow strong and tall like the Oak but will guard against the chaos that always lies close and, in her branches, will one day sit a young girl with golden hair. Closer to the boggy edge I will plant an Alder and amongst its branches will live the Fae, with their own secrets to be told in the stories we hear as children. Then I will plant the Birch, the first tree of any forest and it will bend in the wind as it grows tall and forgive the wind for blowing. I will plant the Willow near a river so that as its branches drop it will spread its message through the lands. And when all the trees are planted, they will speak in the voice of the forest. They will speak across worlds. Which tales will they tell? Well, that is up to all who live in this world. But remember for every tale of woe we hear there are a thousand tales of love and happiness, and our world depends on which we gift. So I take the stories and weave new tales to gift to you, tales of the first forest and all who dwell there still.

And so, let me tell you the secrets of the universe, but first I have a forest to plant.

Interlude 3

Hannah

The stories align

The woman formed from Yggdrasil called herself Gaia and she
longed to be with Thawa as an equal but although she searched
from the highest point, no sign of Thawa could be found in this
world. Gaia returned, downhearted, to her tree and called upon it
for help but the tree appeared tired and many of its leaves lay
upon the ground. Gaia threw herself into the tree and climbed up
through the branches and as she did so the tree's life force
returned, and with it the knowledge of all that was happening in
the many worlds.

Gaia could see that all the worlds were out of balance for when
Thawa had come into the world he had, accidentally, brought
something else with him and that thing was named Chaos.

Chaos had split the worlds from each other and had cut off the
flow of the trees of the forest so that now each forest was alone,
with Thawa split through them all. The only forest in which he did
not reside was the centre, the first forest with its new Gaia. The
very soul of the forest itself.

And Gaia called out in utter desperation for all that had not been
and should have been and her cry made the wind and her tears
made the lakes. When her desperation receded, there came her
anger, and with her anger came thunderous storms that sent
lightning flashing across the skies. This brought fire to the Earth
and all the other worlds heard the thunder and were afraid.
Thawa also heard the thunder but for him it carried a voice, the

voice he had dreamed of and longed for all the years he had been here, and he set out to find the owner of that voice.

Chaos also heard the cries in the thunder and was intrigued and went in search of Gaia. Being able to see multiple worlds, he watched Thawa's search with glee, and formed a plan. In the centre of the world he inhabited was a forest and in the centre of that forest was a clearing and encircling this clearing lived all the trees of the first forest. The only difference between this world and the first world was Yggdrasil, for Gaia's tree existed only in the first forest.

Chaos called from the centre of the forest, "It is me, Thawa, and I am lost!"

Gaia heard the cry and urged Yggdrasil to send out branches to this other world and pluck Chaos back into the first forest. Thinking he was Thawa, she fell into his arms and that evening as the sun went down, they lay together, and the first people were conceived. These first people, conceived in lust, betrayal and deception soon multiplied and spread through the world and started to become like Chaos himself, and as they rampaged through the woods Gaia became afraid. How could she trust the wild children she had dreamed of with these unruly, children of Chaos?

Gaia called to her partner, Chaos, but when he was confronted by the devious, destructive nature of their children he just laughed and told Gaia that they were just how they should be.

Gaia grew saddened and spent more time inside Yggdrasil, closing herself off more and more from the world and the forest that she had so loved.

Many years passed and the tree at the centre of the forest
became quieter and Gaia was not seen for a long time. The
children grew bigger and stronger and ruled the forest. But
Chaos himself forgot to keep blocking communication between
the trees and slowly once again their roots entwined. With the
trees talking once more, word came to Yggdrasil of a man
wandering alone, calling the name of Gaia, and the tree woke the
spirit of the world again and told her what the trees had seen.

In a clearing in a forest many times from her own, Gaia found
her Thawa waiting for her. He had waited, knowing that one day
she would find him and together they returned to the first forest.
They banished the children to the other realms and tried to catch
Chaos, but he was always elusive, managing always to slip away
to start his mischief again. Gaia returned to Yggdrasil and the
tree turned in on itself until all the worlds were enclosed within
the tree and only the first forest lived outside.

A Forest Ghost Story

Foresters will always know a forest ghost story, for the woodlands are full of old magics and the vibrations of all of those that have gone before, but in some places that strangeness and otherworldly feeling comes very close to the surface. Many of the names for these woods show how places can become scary to people. One such place is the Devil's Highway in Windsor Forest, and it is here that this story takes place.

My small caravan was always parked in the forest at Windsor for a couple of months during the summer and early autumn as we prepared the ground for the coming planting season. It was an amazing experience to be in this ancient forest, a forest that for so long had not been open to the public, one of the truest wild woodlands left in this country. Because of this wildness, the forest held on to some of its ancient spirit and as you went deeper into it, you could feel the world drift away, to be replaced by the true nature of the first forests.

On this warm autumn evening I had decided to drive deep into the forest to sleep out under the stars, so I drove in my trusty, rusty old Landover down onto the Devil's Highway and walked into a large area planted with oaks. The air was still and the earth smelled musty and wet beneath the canopy, and after walking for only a few minutes I found myself lost in a place where no moonlight fell and the darkness was all-consuming. It has always been in places like this that I have felt the most peaceful: far away from crowded streets and noisy roads. A true, small piece of paradise where the silence allows you to hear your own heartbeat. I lay down next to a beautiful oak tree, making a pillow of its roots and, feeling relaxed, I started to become drowsy.

Now, you may be thinking I had fallen asleep and all that followed was just a dream, but I can tell you this was not how it happened, for as I lay still upon the ground I could hear, faintly in the distance, a stirring, a sound I did not know. This noise was not of the animals I knew so well from spending years in the forest, but a sort of breathing. Hurrr, hurr, hurr, hurr. A deep, resonant sound, the second always a note or two lower in pitch than the first. I sat up, straining to hear from which direction the sound was coming, but it was in me and all around me, coming from every direction, from the heart of the forest itself. Hurrr, hurr, hurr, hurr.

I have never been afraid in any woodland, but this was different, it felt as if every tree in the whole world had started to breathe at once. It was an unearthly sound, and with this noise pounding in my head I fled back towards the forest track and as I did so the sound became louder, and now a real physical fear overcame me, and I started to run. I ran as if the Devil was chasing me, never realising that my flight was taking me straight onto the Devil's Highway.

I broke cover from the tree line and my momentum kept me moving right into the middle of the track and as I reached it I heard the most terrifying cries, shouts, and growls so deep they travelled right through my body. Then I heard the hoofbeats of galloping horses behind me, and I turned quickly to see...

...to see, Hell on horseback, with large black dogs as outriders and leading them a skeleton horse so large that it needed eight legs to propel it forward, and riding the horse was a giant blowing a huge trumpet.

As the horse passed me, I felt a cold so deep inside that I thought I was frozen to the spot, but then, when I thought the horse had passed, a great arm grabbed me and I was lifted high up into the air and then – like a bullet down a barrel – we headed off in a crazy ride along the forest track. I was held tight in a cold grip and black dogs with coal-black eyes jumped up at my legs.

The horse continued at full speed and ahead I could see the end of the track where it meets the main road and as we reached it I felt myself falling and as I hit the ground, the creatures melted away into darkness.

As I lay there on the ground, I heard the forest once again take a breath. Hurrr. Then it released the breath. Hurrrrrrrr and all became silent except for my beating heart and soon I could hear the creatures of the forest return and all went back to how the forest always was: serene and beautiful and full of hope.

Full Circle

And so here we are full circle, back on the outskirts of Swindon again, at a smaller plantation near Wanborough. This is to be unique little woodland that changes colour as the year progresses, but for now it is just a barren field. I think back to all the great forests I have seen and wonder how this one will look in the years to come. I hope and pray that creatures unseen and seen will find this place and it will become a magical home for them all, a gentle place full of stories created by the children who will come to play here under the boughs of these gentle trees.

As I work, creating the paths and open areas, I think about this time of year. I think about the changes as dark months turn back to light, as the Oak King once again comes to prominence, defeating the Holly King's wintertime. This year I have nowhere I need to be, and the Yuletide season will consist of just me, my little caravan and perhaps some wine to welcome the coming light. It is not a melancholy thought, but it does bring back a lot of memories of times long ago of Christmases with family, friends and children.

I think about those bygone Yules: the bike I got one year, long since rusted and thrown away, the myriad of toys and games, the cameras and the telescope that were must-haves for that year, now long gone. But on a table lies the gift that will never leave.

Books: a gift of stories from my mother and father, the diary of planting from Grandfather. These are the gifts that sustained me in both good and bad times. *The Wind in the Willows*, which my father read to me each night, along with *Paddington* and *The Tales of Olga de Polga*, and sitting next to them a stone, washed by the sea. This grey stone with white flashes was a gift given to me by someone who had held it while thinking of me and wishing me well. A little silver necklace on a chain, the sign of the bard, a gift given to me to mark my role as a storyteller, and next to all of those a ring made of paper and decorated with little spirals, a ring I made myself. This ring one day to be given to someone who dreams and imagines the world as I do, a hope, a prayer for our future together, and a small broken shell.

And as I look upon these gifts I think how lucky I have been to be given such beautiful things and wonder if, on this cold night next to a field, someone might think of me and smile at the special times we had, for here in my little home and in many other places around the country I had found my own very special Walden, a place of creativity, of longing for a better world and of peace.

Swept away are the trappings of a successful life: the house, the job, the car, the television constantly broadcasting hatred and the collection of necessary junk that always seemed so essential at the time, to be replaced by an ever-nurturing earth and a longing for stories to feed the soul.

Being in the forest has always been about learning, about ourselves and about the world as it is. The forests are never subtle in their teaching: they push us to look within ourselves and to find all those things we both love and dislike in who we are and who we want to be. They make sense of our rushing world and teach us to step back and to quieten minds that are driven almost mad by the incessant information we are expected to deal with.

And so here I am, just me in my forest to be, on Christmas Day. The trees have arrived, and I am now going to start planting. It seems like such an auspicious day to begin. I look towards the houses along the little lane next to the new wood and see that the pub is now closed, no lights in the window, and along the lane a few houses with lights on and decorations in their windows, and I hope that their day is full of the joy I feel to be here.

For the first time in any wood I have planted, I start in the centre, with one small oak sapling and I smile as I imagine how big and strong it will grow.

Hours pass and I am lost in the task, when I hear a voice behind me. Turning, I see an old lady. I have seen her before, walking up the lane hand in hand with her husband and I have longed to one day be part of a couple like this, growing old, loving and happy. "There is a place set for you at our table and we would be really happy if you came," says the old lady. And I accept, because despite all my longing for solitude, I also feel great love for the people of this world and for the memories and stories that they share.

Epilogue

Years have passed and the caravan long gone but, in its place, sits a wooden cabin, a cabin now shared with the artist I had dreamed of so many times. We could talk now of where we eventually met and all those things, but every story needs a bit of hidden romance and love to keep it alive.

Those tales and stories from the woods grow stronger in us each day and they feed our souls that also longed to find each other. I wonder If my other in the first forest found his muse and I have written about it in the journal and hope I see myself replying one day but I think his first and only love was Gaia and that tree in the centre of the first forest. I have made many forests over the years some alone and some now with Hannah, but as time has passed being the man who planted trees became harder and harder to do and eventually it gave up on how slow I had become. So now my days are full writing the stories of the forest and this is where we find ourselves today.

We have walked through the first forest together and Gaia has grown used to the two of us here but today we walked farther than ever, deep into the woods. The trees grew stiller as we walked until eventually, they opened out onto a vast lake and before us with mists coming down, we could make out seals and hear their eerie calls floating across the water. There is a boat at a jetty here and we walk over to it. Birds dip in and out of the water and it looks so tempting.

The Tales of
The Trees

Birch

So here we sit, grandfather and I, looking out across the meadow, our backs to the silvery skin of the tall birch tree. Its bark feels smooth and cold, not unpleasant but strangely comforting and Grandfather starts to tell me the story of the Birch.

"Beith," he pronounces it 'Bey', "is the first forest's first tree, here long before people even before the first creatures. At first the Beith had no idea about how to grow, so it looked around at the other plants and tried to grow like them, with many stems reaching towards the sky. It could not decide whether to be tall or short, wide or thin. As it grew it soon realised that it could tower over all the other plants and see for miles around. With its silvery shining skin it could be seen far and wide by the first folk who had seen nothing like it before.

Tentatively they came closer to Beith and beneath its shining limbs they found shelter from the hottest sun and the wildest wind.
As time went by the first folk, who called themselves "the Greef", learned that not only could Beith give them shelter but also that cooling waters made from the silver bark could ease the troubles of their stomachs; and so the Beith gave them the first medicines.

As time went by the Beiths grew thicker and started to cover the land. They offered protection from the harsh early world, and so the first creatures came to live amongst them: the deer, the birds, the bees and the bears. All the creatures adored the Beith, for in the branches, in the bark or in the roots all could find a home. And as the trees grew so the roots entwined, deep underground, the trees started to speak to one another across many, many miles.

And so the first forest was born.

And here in the forest the trees started to change the land and desert became fertile and hillsides became green as the cycle of living trees formed the early soil. The trees with their newfound height breathed the new air high up in the sky and so the thick air, that had once surrounded all of the lands became like nectar for the creatures of the earth and in their turn they grew bigger and bolder upon this new world

Hope

BIRCH

change

Purification

New Ideas

Rowan

Late in the evening we are sitting in the meadow a little way away from the birch tree and now for the first time I can see that the meadow is set out like a clock, with different trees in a round. The tree that we are now sitting beside I learn is called Luis.

"The Beith had been alone for a long time and the stories the roots told were a sad one. Some of the creatures that flew high above or lived down below were feeling great hunger as they became more abundant but food became more scarce. They had searched and searched for new foods yet those plants became rare as the Beith took up more of the land. Even the Greef were finding it hard, especially in the darker times of the year. The warm times were still good but they did not last long and soon once again cold would reign.

So on the hottest day, the tallest Beith raised itself up from the tallest mountain and called out to the Sun for help. The Sun looked down and saw that times would soon be hard, so he shone as bright as he could onto the tallest Beith on that tallest mountain and suddenly the tree was transformed by the power of the Sun's light. This new tree was called Luis and had beautiful white flowers that were loved by the bees, and in the harshest winter bright red berries to feed the birds.

Touched thus by the Sun, the Luis was not totally of this Earth and formed the bridge between the worlds of light and dark, holding the magic of intuition and the protection from the dark. The Greef came to know it as "the knowledgeable tree which held within itself power and success".

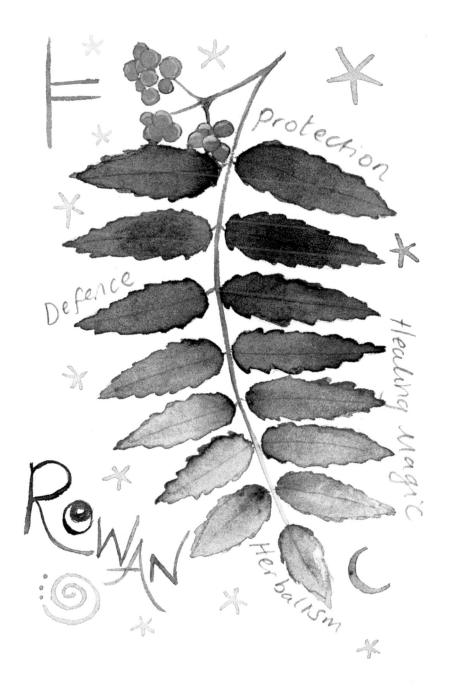

Protection

Defence

Healing Magic

Herbalism

ROWAN

Alder

Moving around the meadow, we finally come across a wetter spot and Grandfather takes out a cloak from his pack and lays it on the ground for us to sit on. "See the purple in this tree," he says. "This is the Fearn", which he pronounces verern.

"One day the Rowan tree wanted to know why it was here and what its purpose might be. It had been blessed by the sun and loved the warmth upon its trunk. But this one Rowan had been growing close to water and the roots found loose earth to grow in, so instead of growing as tall as it could it grew down into the damp earth. Down and down the roots stretched, far lower than any of the roots of other trees, until lost and alone, it became afraid, for it has lost all connection to the other trees of the first forest. Eventually, no longer of this world, it grew into the underworld.

Here, it was transformed by the Greef, the strange small people, who guided it back to the world we know and clothed it in purple, which was the colour most loved by them. They came up to reside with this new tree, and now its roots joined the others of the first forest. This tree was different, though: for it held the secrets of the underworld. Each branch and leaf held the power to teach and to learn from all of those that had gone before. For the Greef, it became the tree that they went to when they needed guidance.

ALDER

Change

Hope

Rebirth

Willow

Still in the wetter section of the meadow, we have now moved a bit further around the clock, and this time are seated beneath a sweeping curtain of fine leaves, and this tree I am told is called Saille.

"One night a short time after the little people had arrived with the Fearne one of their young fell into the churning river and the Beith were afraid for her but none of them knew what to do to save her. One of the Beith in pure grief grew as tall as it could and called out to the shimmering moon for help. The shimmering Moon grew bright and her light touched the top of this one Beith, and suddenly it was transformed. The branches grew heavier with leaf and they bent down into the waters to catch the fallen fae. The poor child, swept up, now wept into this new tree's leaves and in response they grew long and those tears dripped off the ends and back to the waters. The child was returned to the fae, who in pure joy bestowed gifts upon the new tree of the first forest.

Even the smallest twig broken off the Saille could regrow for it held the understanding of birth and death, new beginnings and hope, but the greatest of the fae's gift came from the child herself, for she was named Aine Chlair and her tears gave the Saille the chance to live on both the land and in the water, to live in separate worlds, joining them together.

Enchantment

healing

cycles of the Moon

psychic power

Willow

Ash

Moving out of the wettest section of the meadow we now come to one of the largest trees. It stands tall, its straight trunk reaching high into the sky. Grandfather tells me this one is called Nuin. "The little people, who are sometimes called the fae, had grown used to living within the trees but they worried that they were losing their connection to their families from the underworld. The Beith of the forest sensed this and really wanted to help but could not think of a way. So, they sent messages out to the Fearn to see if they could help, but the Fearn were scared to go back, for the journey was arduous and it was so easy to get lost.

On the land, the Greef had also changed. They called out to the Sun to help them understand their changes, but the whole of the new world was also in flux. Great earthquakes, boiling heat and freezing cold would happen so often that the Greef thought the heavens were falling. They called upon the first forest to help them and the Beith heard their cries.

The Beith and the Fearn decided that if one grew high into the sky and one grew low into the ground then their roots would connect, and they could hold each other in perfect balance. And so they grew, one upwards towards the heavens and one downwards into the ground. For both it was a long and arduous journey but as the Fearn hit the underworld and the Beith hit the heavens a great cracking sound was heard as the two became one mighty tree, holding the three worlds in place and in perfect balance. This is how the first forest produced Yggdrasil, the great world tree.

ASH

Yggdrasil

Fate

Inspiration

Spiritual

Renewal

Peace

Hawthorn

I wanted to sit with my back against the trunk to hear the story as I had with all the trees before, but this little tree was different: it was thorny and spiky, almost as if it did not want me to sit beneath it. "You feel its difference," Grandfather said. "It is not like the other trees and there is a good reason for that, for this is the first tree that other trees did not make. This little tree, so gnarled and thorned, but full of blossom in the spring and berries of brightest red in the winter, carries the magic of the fae, for it was they who brought this tree to life.

As time passed in the first forest, the Greef, who now called themselves the People, started to encroach further and further into the land. They did not dislike the Fae but could not understand them and their need to be close to the ground or living inside the trees. The Fae had become more worried about losing the lovely places they held dear and so they took the small pieces of the Fearn and sharpened them into points. They took the berries from the Luis and searched for the smallest Beith. Upon finding one, very, very close to the World Tree, they attached all of their creations to it. The Fae then called on the ancestor's low down in Yggdrasil to help them and the little Beith transformed into the gnarled, spiky tree which they named Uath. The little Uath grew quickly and from its berries more grew and soon the tree encircled the World Tree and the places in which the Fae resided. The People now cried out, for they felt cut off from the Sun and the World Tree, but the Fae, pleased with themselves, dwelt happily with the Uath.

Hawthorn

Faery

Purification

Protection

Oak

Now this was better, I thought to myself. This tree, huge and tall, was good to sit under, comforting and strong. This is the tree I would want to be were I given that choice.

"You seem comfortable under this tree," Grandfather said, I nodded. "Well, so you should, as this is the mighty Dair and this tree was made by your ancestors and that is why it feels so comfortable, but it took a long time to become the tree you see today."

In the deep of the forest, the Fae now felt safe in their haven, surrounded by the Uath trees which grew close together and formed an impenetrable barrier against the People, but beyond the Uath, the People grew scared and were constantly worried about what the Fae were doing behind their barrier. The People decided that something had to be done, as every time they had tried to penetrate the barrier, new, even thornier trees had grown up in front of them.

A beacon tree was needed, the People decided, one so tall and strong that they could climb up into its boughs in order to see what those tricky Fae were up to. So, under the light of the strongest Sun, they took a twig from the World Tree, the strongest part of the Beith, and commanded the new tree to grow as strong and as tall as it could.

Under this great tree the people practised their magics and from it grew the first white-robed priests, those of the People who spoke for the gods.

The Oak tree flourished. Through summer and winter it grew taller and stronger, and parts of the forest became dark under its boughs.

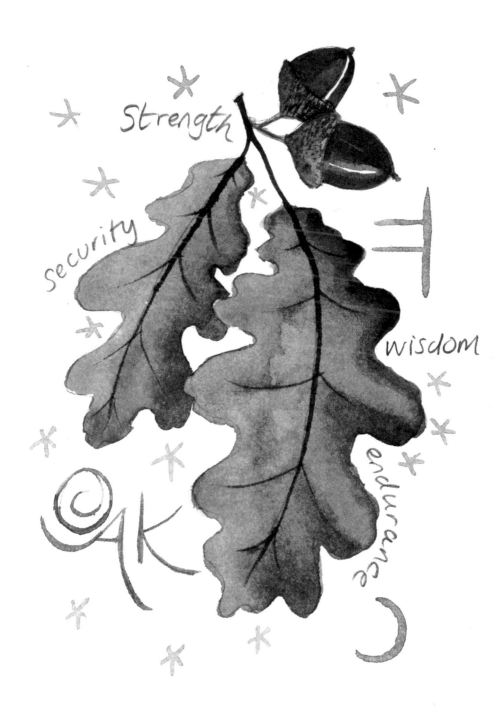

Holly

From the Oak tree grandfather took me diagonally across the circle of trees, rather than around them, as we had been going. Finally, we ended up next to a tree I knew well, "The Holly" I exclaimed. For here was the tree that throughout winter was filled with bright red berries and for Christmas a small sprig always sat above the door of grandfather's house.

Many years passed and the oak tree grew stronger and taller, as it grew so the season changed, and winter never came. All the other trees of the forest grew weary and tired and the ground became hard and dry. The warmth of each day stopped the peoples, creatures and the Fae from their daily routines and soon they became afraid. The Fae and the people had not spoken for such a long time but now they came together once again to try to stop the oak from destroying their world.

This is how the tree of winter was formed, in the depths of what should have been winter a small section of the oak tree was cut away and transplanted onto a thorn from the hawthorn tree. This new tree was named Tinne and slowly it grew beneath the bows of its brother. Now these twin brothers battled for light and battled for ground. As the years passed the Tinne grew strong and on the turning wheel, at the summer solstice it finally defeated his brother and slowly the oak went to sleep and holly became the king of the winter.

Holly

Balance

Talent

Transformation

Courage

Hazel

Moving back across the circle heading for the oak again a smaller tree sits to the side, this small tree takes up a lot of room with its multiple branches coming from the centre and we cannot sit with our backs against it as we have the other trees. On the ground beneath us is many small nut cases opened over the winter and eaten by hungry creatures.

This tree I learn is called Coll, grandfather says its name comes from the word collect, collection and collective and it is the tree of wisdom and treaties.

The people and the Fae had finally got winter to return and after a few years, balance was once again restored as each year Holly would defeat Oak for winter and Oak would defeat Holly for the summer.

The people and the Fae were once again in harmony and a celebration was called, this celebration was to take place on each of the turnings of the wheel, one for the coming light and one for the waning light and a tree was produced to honour the treaty. This tree was a tree of deepest wisdom for it held the secret of balance and care and this is how the little Hazel arrived in the first forest, always to live on the edges keeping the secrets of the land.

wisdom

Divination

Creativity

Ritual

Hazel

Apple

There is a tree in the clearing that almost always catches my eye when we first enter and it is because, as spring starts it goes white with small flowers and as the year passes small red and green fruits grow on its boughs. This is the tree we come to next. Sometimes I feel sad in the autumn for grandfather would never let me eat the fruits of this tree and always said, it is a gift for the creatures and insects of the forest. He would tell me that I had plenty of apples from other trees. He tells me this tree is named Quert.

Time passes in the forest and peace reigned between the Fae and the people and all lived alongside each other in friendly cooperation, the Fae felt part of the land for the first time and decided to gift the people with a tree from their world. This was the Quert tree and not only contained fruits to eat but also great healing magics. The tree that they brought forth contained all the beauty of their own realms. Soon a great celebration was held.

During the celebration to mark the great union of all things from all worlds the Fae taught the people some of their charms and the people learned new ways of healing and of divination. This allowed the peoples of the world to forecast weather and so become safe from the storms that sometimes came and the people vowed to give a gift back to the Fae.

APPLE

Magic

Love

Divination

Healing

Beauty

Vine

Once again as we stop, we are not by any tree but by a thicket of thorns, bramble and growing from that another plant which I do not recognise, "no way will I be leaning with my back to this one" I say and grandfather smiles, "two trees in one" he says, "and perhaps the most confusing of all the forests trees". Confusing, yes, I think as this looks nothing like a tree at all.

The Muin tree is the most confused and confusing of all the trees of the forest I learn as it is two trees in one name, and it all came about from the magics of the little apple tree. The little apple tree a gift to the peoples of the earth, found it was never left alone and having the beauty in the spring and fruit throughout the autumn, it could never do the one thing it wanted and that was to feed the creatures of the forest. It decided it needed to be better protected and with the highest fruit on its highest bough it grew a seed unlike any other and no person or Fae could ever reach this tiny apple with its magic seed. When the winter came, and all its leaves gone the seed dropped down to the earth and there it grew in the soil. It grew low and thick with thorns so much sharper that the hawthorn and under it all the creatures scurried and hid. The people were of course unhappy so to appease them the new Muin tree grew black fruit, so very sweet and from that fruit grew vines which bore the climbing fruit and so the bramble and vine were born.

Ivy

I am now very confused, and I look to grandfather for an explanation, for we are now stood once again at the Oak tree. I see the glint in his eye and know I have missed something. "Look around" he says. I walk around the tree but see nothing odd and definitely no other trees. "You are so used to this one that you just don't see it" he says and then I know. Spiralling up the hard trunk of the oak tree is the ivy. I stare upwards, high into the boughs and still cannot see where it ends. "It is called Gort" he tells me and this was a gift".

From the new apple tree, the people of the world learned the first ways to harvest and grow new trees and so pleased with this gift, they decided something should be given to the Fae in return. During many days they talked of what could be given and what the Fae needed but could come up with nothing new as the Fae never seemed to hunger or tire, they just seemed to play and enjoy the world. They always lived low in the ground or even under the Earth itself but soon the people had a plan.

They took root of the vine and leaf from birch and there they formed a brand-new plant and they named it Gort. This new plant grew shoots from the ground and climbed all of the trees, especially loving the oak and soon the Fae were climbing and swinging about in this new tree. The tree grew thick and as the years passed many Fae left their home on the ground and lived high in the trees of the forest.

Ivy

Wildness

Abundance

Spirals

Reawakening

Broom

"Once again, not a tree" I say to grandfather, and he smiles.
"Perhaps not a tall tree, but a very important one in the circle of
trees as this is maybe the one that started up all the problems
between the fae and the People again. This is called nGeatal" and he
pronounces it Knee eh tal.

Each year the apple trees, that had grown abundant in the forest,
grew large, tasty fruit that was so loved by everyone, but for the
people harvest time was not easy. Growing around every one of these
trees was the bramble and vine. The Fae and many other of the
small creatures never seemed to have a problem getting to the fruit
but for the people it was a painful experience. They grumbled every
year about the Fae, always at play and never working hard and
then getting the apples with never a single scratch.

One spring morning when the bramble lay dormant still, the people
took the brightest yellowest blossoms from the apple tree and planted
them in two avenues right up to the base of the tree. These brightest
flowers had come from the tops of the tree and were especially blessed
by the Sun. As summer past the avenues grew and upon the ground
there grew no brambles and when harvest time was upon them, they
took all of the fruit with not a single scratch.

Vitality

Healers

Strength

Health

BROOM

Blackthorn and Elder

Way past the Oak, the bramble and down in the lower south side of the circle, we find ourselves at something that can only be described as a thicket, multiple stems with green leaves and small fruit but surrounding them all these wickedly sharp spikes. Next to this tree is another bearing black fruit but without spines. Grandfather calls the first one Straif and the other Ruis.

The people of the world had picked all the apples and left nothing for the fae or the creatures, now that they had found a way to supress the bramble. The Fae elders were angry and called for a meeting with the people. They sent out a child messenger to ask the people to come, but upon the earth a new being had arrived and this being called itself chaos. Chaos saw the opportunity and stole the child away leaving behind just the child's tunic and one of the people's cloaks. The Fae found the child and believed the people had taken him and in haste and with anger two trees were formed.

The first of these new trees was a tree that only the Fae could eat from, it having bitter fruit and protected by vicious thorns and the second tree they filled with magic. This magic was held in the flowers and berries and anyone who ate from it would be filled with introspection and remorse. Ever gentle the Fae hoped the people would feel sorry for what they had done.

Secrecy
Underworld
Spirits
Omens
Blackthorn

Gorse and Heather

"Once again, no trees here" I say as we walk around the circle and stand before a very barren patch of land. It has low growing plants interspersed with larger spiky ones, which look very similar to the broom tree. "This is the Onn and the Uhr trees" I am told.

With Ailm, the young fae child missing, the Fae started searching and during the search they came across a beautiful young Fae man, but this was a man no other Fae recognised. "I saw the people take her" he said, "out of the forest and towards the mountains". The Fae immediately rushed to the edge of the forest. From here the mountains grew tall and nothing grew upon the land and the Fae started searching. High up on the hill Ailm's roots grew out under the ground towards her family and as they reached them and their tears fell upon the ground, small plants, so pretty and delicate formed and the Fae stopped to look, these plants were so delicate, just like little Ailm.

Now chaos still looking like a beautiful Fae man came striding out to cause more troubles and as he got nearer so a spiky bush appeared in front of him and every time he tried to get close to the Fae another would hinder his progress and he grew angry, and as his anger grew so he changed and suddenly in front of the Fae was a grotesque man, full of hate and loathing and they knew that he was the one who took Ailm away.

Hope

Purification

Spiritual Path

Divination

Gorse

Relationships

Good Luck

Faery

Magic

Heather

Pine

"Now that's a tree" I say to grandfather as we stand beside an enormous trunk that seems to reach right up to the sky. "This one is called Ailm" he tells me "And the story starts as a very sad tale".

Chaos has stolen away a young child from the Fae and hidden the child deep within a mountain, high up in the hills. Chaos left her there to go and see the mischief he had caused and while the troubles brewed in the forest, Chaos forgot all about the little child.

Lost and alone this child, who was named Ailm, shivered and as she tired with the cold and lack of food lay down upon the soil covered ground and stared upwards towards the only light, a hole high above her. Days passed and as she grew weaker, she called out to the night sky for help and in that moment the hole filled with light as a disc appeared high in the sky.

The light that shone on this night was still unformed but had been brought about by longing and need, it showed Ailm the way and she listened and planted her feet firmly in the soil and as the days passed, she grew towards the light. She grew way out of the top of the mountain and was reborn as the tree of the mountains, a young tree full of hope and excitement.

Spiritual awakening

Joy

Clarity

Resolution

Scots Pine

Aspen

I stand looking at the tree we have arrived at now and it seems a sudden breeze has sprung up around it. The tree seems to be moving, almost trembling as if afraid, the leaves rustling and shaking. I touch it, almost afraid for it. "This is the Eadhadh tree" grandfather tell me, pronouncing it eedar.

The Fae realised that Chaos was a trickster and afraid they backed away from him, as he turned and changed into many forms before them, but he was constantly held back by the new growing Gorse. Chaos shouted and spat out hatred and threats towards the Fae.

Deep in the forest the People heard the commotion and came quickly to the plains and there they recognised Chaos, for he had hurt them before. The people went quickly to the Fae and embraced them as friends. They told the Fae the truth of who Chaos was and exposed, he disappeared from them. The Fae immediately knew it was not the people that had taken Ailm. They looked to the mountains and for the first time noticed the new tree and called out to it and through the ground more of the heather grew.

One of the Fae though in total fear had become rooted to the spot, for she was the mother of Ailm and from her grew a new tree, one that lived on the plains overlooked by her daughter.

endurance

flexibility

Enlightenment

perception

Aspen

Yew

"The last tree of the first forest" Grandfather says, "or the first tree".
Confused I ask the question "You can only be last or first but never
both". "Well," he says "what is the first and last place in a circle" I
still do not understand. "You will, one day he says". He tells me this
tree is called Idad.

The Fae and the people of the world stood upon the plain and looked
to the mountain where Ailm now resided, not Fae anymore,
transformed into something new and they could also see Eadhadh
also changed and transformed. They all knew of death and loss and
sorrow but had never before seen change in their own kinds. As
darkness fell, they stayed in the open for the first time in many
years and suddenly a new light shone above them, the light of the
moon created from Ailm's sadness.

As they stood amazed a new presence appeared and she was golden
haired and surrounding her were all the creatures of the world, to
the Fae she was like them and to the people like one of them and in
her hand she held a twig of vibrant green and in her other a bright
red stone and she planted these upon the earth and called out "To
remember all that once were and all that will be". From then on
wherever this new tree lived it became a sacred place of remembrance
and peace.

Yew

Rebirth

Endings

Ancestors

transitions

Mistletoe

I had thought that we had now encountered all the trees of the forest, but Grandfather told me there was one more and to see if I could find it. I had spent over an hour looking while he just stood by the old apple tree and waited. Eventually I gave up. "I have been stood by it all this time" he said. "look up into the tree" I looked and saw a tangle of branches, not apple branches, high up in the tree. "That is the mistletoe" he tells me "And it is important to me but was not present in the first forest"

"This tree, magical, as it lives between the sky and the Earth and was revered by all healers and called All Heal" he tells me.

Many years and then many centuries passed, the forest was a peaceful place, full of stories and magic. The Fae, the People and all the creatures lived happily amongst the forest of the world. Chaos had been banished to the other worlds, unable to return he rampaged and wherever he went anger and hurt followed. The Fae were afraid for the dwellers of other realms and they sent out a bird to look over the other world. This small thrush saw the sorrow of these worlds and upon the branches of the trees she left a gift, a gift of healing and a gift of hope. A small tree grew between the heavens and earth and this tree gifted all that could see, a gateway to the first forest and a light in the darkest of days.

Mistletoe

ALL heal

protection

love

fertility

A meditation on the World

It seems so often that the world of man is a noisy and busy world, one where nearly every place must compete to be heard. The forests are also noisy, but it is a different noise, from the scurrying creatures on the ground, to the bird's sound and wing beats. Sometimes the sound of a fox barking or the rustle of air through leaves. These are the sounds I love, not the cars engines or people shouting to be heard, but the calming natural sounds of the forest, alive and vital.

Deep within all the trees of the forest lays the heartbeat and the gateway to all the worlds and so here I sit at this great oak, back against its hard trunk and slowly feel myself sinking deep inside. Sounds from outside become muted but an inner noise starts to fill my head, and this is the heartbeat of the tree, as sap is pushed upwards, and nutrients fed downwards. This is a true pulse like humans and the pressure regulated by the lifting of branch and leaf through night and day and on this day, I decide to follow the upward path through the tree.

Travelling higher and higher and getting smaller and smaller, I find myself taking a turn along a smaller branch and then into a twig on the very edge of the tree's expanse and for the first time a small amount of light fills my sight. The light grows brighter, yet greener as I enter the smallest veins of the very oaks leaf. High above the ground, seeing through the myriad of glowing cells I hang from the leaf as the smallest drop of water. And then falling, free and as light as air, the whole world to explore.